ALL MY LIFE
I'VE FELT THAT
DEEP WITHIN
ME I'VE BEEN
SUPPRESSING
A GREAT
EVIL.

THAT'S WHY
I WAS
AFRAID
WHEN MOTHER
HAD MY
PORTRAIT
PAINTED.

BUT MY PORTRAIT MADE ME LOOK **YOUNG** AND **GOOD** AND **INNOCENT.** IT REMINDED ME OF THAT STORY - **YOU** REMEMBER - " THE PORTRAIT OF DORIAN GRAY "—

—WHERE THIS YOUNG MAN WITH GREAT EVIL IN HIM NEVER AGED A DAY - BUT HIS **PORTRAIT** GREW OLD AND UGLY AND **EVIL.**

Hold Me!

JULES FEIFFER

RANDOM HOUSE   NEW YORK

Other books by Jules Feiffer:
SICK, SICK, SICK
PASSIONELLA AND OTHER STORIES
THE EXPLAINERS
BOY, GIRL. BOY, GIRL.

Published in association with Hall Editions, Inc.

The author wishes to thank The Hall Syndicate, Inc., *The Village Voice*,
Playboy magazine, and *The London Observer* for permission
to reprint the strips in this book.

SO I **HID** MY PORTRAIT, DETERMINED **NEVER** TO LOOK AT IT AGAIN. AND AS THE YEARS WENT BY I WENT TO WORK, I CAME HOME, I WENT TO WORK, I CAME HOME. BUT I DID NOT AGE A DAY.

I **CRINGED** AT WHAT MY PORTRAIT MUST LOOK LIKE. I GOT MARRIED, I WENT TO WORK, I CAME HOME. I HAD CHILDREN, I WENT TO WORK, I CAME HOME. BUT I DID NOT AGE A DAY.

FINALLY I COULD
STAND IT **NO** LONGER!
I **HAD** TO KNOW
MY **REAL** SOUL
AND IT WAS ON
THAT CANVAS! I
RIPPED THE
PAINTING FROM
ITS HIDING PLACE
AND **REMOVED**
THE COVER!

IT
WAS
BLANK.

I BURNED
THE CANVAS
BUT IT
MADE NO
DIFFERENCE.
I DID NOT
AGE A
DAY.

I JUST
GO TO
WORK
AND I
COME
HOME.

PLEASE LET
GO, DOLLY.

YOU'VE GOT TO
LET GO SOMETIME!
LOVE IS MORE
THAN MERE
POSSESSION.

LOVE IS GIVING RATHER
THAN TAKING, FREEING
RATHER THAN ENSLAVING.
LOVE IS -OOMPH-
PLEASE LOOSEN
YOUR GRIP, DOLLY.

IF YOU'RE AFRAID TO LET GO
IT MEANS YOU DON'T TRUST
ME, IF YOU DON'T TRUST
ME IT MEANS YOU THINK
I'LL LEAVE YOU, AND IF
YOU THINK I'LL LEAVE
YOU IT MEANS YOU
DON'T HAVE ANY
RESPECT FOR YOURSELF—

I USED TO WORK FOR THE F.B.I. - ASSIGNED TO THE PEACE MOVEMENT - UNDERGROUND AGENT TO CHECK OUT COMMUNIST INFILTRATION

ALL PRETTY ROUTINE - MASS MEETINGS - PICKETING THE WHITE HOUSE - KENNEDY SERVING COFFEE - NO RESULTS WHATEVER -

THEN I MET EDNA - SOFT - COMPELLING - DOCTRINAIRE - ; SHE FELL IN LOVE. I FELL IN LOVE. WE DECIDED ON MARRIAGE.

BUT MY SECRET SEPARATED US. I HAD TO TELL HER. I PROCEEDED TO DO SO. ON OUR WEDDING NIGHT I REPORTED "EDNA, I AM AN UNDERGROUND AGENT FOR YOUR F.B.I.

EDNA WEPT. THEN SHE TOLD ME **HER** SECRET. "SAM," SHE REPORTED, "I AM AN UNDERGROUND COMMUNIST ASSIGNED TO INFILTRATE THE PEACE MOVEMENT.

YOU CAN IMAGINE WHAT FOLLOWED. A LOVERS QUARREL. I INSISTED EDNA GIVE UP **HER** WORK. SHE. INSISTED I GIVE UP **MINE**.

WE CONSULTED A MARRIAGE COUNSELOR. HE ADVISED US TO COMPROMISE— "ALL FORMS OF EXTREMISM ARE MISGUIDED" HE REPORTED. "QUIT YOUR RESPECTIVE JOBS AND JOIN A COMMUNITY CENTER."

I COULDNT. EDNA COULDNT. WE SAID GOOD-BYE AND I TURNED HER IN.

ILL ALWAYS WAIT FOR YOU EDNA

MEN DON'T
UNDERSTAND
ME. THEY
THINK I
TALK TOO
MUCH.

MEN DON'T UNDERSTAND
THEY SHOULDN'T LISTEN
TO WHAT I SAY- THEY
SHOULD LISTEN TO
WHAT I **MEAN**!

WHAT I SAY IS
BLA BLA BLA-
WHAT I MEAN
IS BEAUTY
AND POETRY.

WHAT I SAY IS
GIBBLE GABBLE GIBBLE-
WHAT I MEAN IS
I AM A LOST SOUL.
STUDY MY HAUNTED
EYES.

WHAT I SAY IS
HA HA HA HA –
WHAT I MEAN
IS LIFE IS A
WASTE AND
NOBODY CARES
A **FIG** FOR ME.

SOMEDAY I'LL MEET A
MAN WHO WILL IGNORE
MY STUPID WORDS AND
KNOW INSTANTLY THE
FRAGILE, DELICATE,
PERFECTION THAT
LIES BEHIND THEM.

HE WILL SEE
THROUGH ME.
AND OURS
WILL BE A
BEAUTIFUL
LOVE –

I'LL
HURT
HIM.

HELLO- SYLVIA? THIS IS BERNARD.

THIS IS SYLVIA WALLENDER-

HONEY I'M SORRY ABOUT WHAT I SAID. BELIEVE ME I COULD CUT MY TONGUE OUT.

I AM NOT AT HOME AT THE MO-MENT-

I KNOW I SAID I'D NEVER APOLOGIZE-BUT I CAN'T LIVE **WITHOUT** YOU! DO YOU UNDER-STAND?

BUT I WILL RETURN SHORTLY-

I WAS WRONG. **SO** WRONG- I **LOVE** YOU, SYLVIA! LOVE YOU, LOVE YOU, LOVE YOU!

IF YOU WOULD LIKE TO LEAVE A MESSAGE PLEASE WAIT TILL YOU HEAR THE SIGNAL ON THIS RECORDING. YOU HAVE THIRTY SECONDS.

SYLVIA?

IT DIDN'T **SEEM**
LIKE THIRTY
SECONDS.

YES, SIR, THIS IS THE TELEPHONE COMPANY BUSINESS OFFICE. MAY I BE OF HELP?

YES. I'D LIKE TO RENT A PLACE TO LIVE.

I'M SORRY, SIR. WE ARE NOT A REAL ESTATE COMPANY. WE ARE A TELEPHONE COMPANY.

BUT THAT'S WHAT I WANT TO RENT- A TELEPHONE BOOTH. A **SIDEWALK GLASS** TELEPHONE BOOTH.

CAN'T YOU RECEIVE YOUR CALLS **INDOORS**, SIR? WE HAVE **MANY** ATTRACTIVE VARI-COLORED **PRIVATE** PHONES —

NOBODY EVER **CALLS** ME INDOORS! PEOPLE THINK I'M **ALOOF**! I GIVE THE WRONG **IMPRESSION**! IF I STAY COOPED UP IN A CLOSED APART- MENT, HOW WILL THEY EVER KNOW I'M OPEN TO FRIENDSHIP? BUT IF I MOVED INTO A PUBLIC TELEPHONE BOOTH —

YES, I SEE. WELL, YOUR TELEPHONE COMPANY WILL DO ALMOST ANYTHING TO MAKE MONEY, SIR, BUT I DON'T KNOW IF WE CAN —

DON'T YOU **WANT** ME TO HAVE **FRIENDS!**

I DO BELIEVE YOU'RE IN LUCK, SIR. WE HAPPEN TO HAVE A **CHOICE** LOCATION IN THE EAST SIXTIES. YOU DON'T HAVE ANY DOGS OR CHILDREN, DO YOU?

I DON'T HAVE **ANYTHING!** THAT'S **WHY** I WANT A TELEPHONE BOOTH! **HOW** MUCH?

THAT WILL BE TEN CENTS FOR THE FIRST THREE MINUTES AND FIVE CENTS FOR EACH SUCCEEDING THREE MINUTES — PLUS THE USUAL MONTH'S SECURITY IN ADVANCE. IS THERE ANYTHING ELSE?

YOU WOULDN'T KNOW WHERE I COULD RENT ONE OF THOSE BLUE AND RED **MAIL BOXES** WOULD YOU?

MARVIN, **WHO** I HAVE ASKED YOU **IS** IT?

NO, MOTHER. NOTHING TO WORRY ABOUT. I **KNOW** YOU TOLD ME WHAT TO EXPECT. I **KNOW** SHE NEEDS FIRM HANDLING.

MARVIN!

HONEST, MOTHER, IT'S BEST YOU **DON'T** TALK TO HER. YOU **KNOW** HOW YOU TWO GO AT EACH OTHER – **SURE**, MOTHER, I **REALIZE** SHE STARTS IT.

FOR THE **LAST** TIME, MARVIN –

GOOD TO HEAR **YOUR** VOICE **TOO**, MOTHER. I'LL WRITE AGAIN AT THE END OF THE WEEK. LISTEN, THANKS FOR THE PRESENTS FOR THE KIDS –

WHO WAS IT?

YOUR MOTHER.

I USED TO
BE VERY
ATHLETIC —
A **MODEL**
OF
AMERICAN
YOUTH!

BUT **THEN** CAME THE **CONGO**
CRISIS WHEN IT SEEMED
THAT WAR WAS **INEVITABLE.**
MY **EYES** STARTED BOTHER-
ING ME AND I HAD TO
GIVE UP READING THE
PAPERS AND GET **GLASSES.**

BUT EXCEPT FOR MY EYES I
WAS **STILL** IN PRETTY
GOOD SHAPE — AND THEN
CAME THE **LAOTIAN**
CRISIS. IT SEEMED THAT
WAR WAS **INEVITABLE.**
MY HEARING STARTED
BOTHERING ME AND I HAD
TO GIVE UP LISTENING
TO RADIO NEWS AND GET
A **HEARING** AID.

BUT OUTSIDE OF BUMPING INTO THINGS AND NEVER QUITE KNOWING WHAT WAS GOING ON I WAS **STILL** IN **FAIRLY GOOD** SHAPE. AND THEN CAME THE **BERLIN** CRISIS. MY BACK GAVE OUT. MY STOMACH TURNED SOUR. AND I DEVELOPED **MIGRAINE**.

THEN I HEARD SOMEWHERE THAT CRITICS WERE ATTACK-ING AMERICAN YOUTH FOR BEING OUT OF SHAPE —

I CAN'T **SEE** — I CAN'T **HEAR** — I CAN'T **BREATHE** — I CAN'T **STAND** — AND I DON'T WANT ANYTHING MORE THAN TO GO INTO A FALLOUT SHELTER AND **VANISH** —

WHAT DO THEY MEAN **OUT OF SHAPE**? I LOOK UPON MYSELF AS THE MAN OF THE FUTURE.

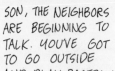

SON, THE NEIGHBORS ARE BEGINNING TO TALK. YOU'VE GOT TO GO OUTSIDE AND PLAY BASEBALL.

BUT I DON'T **LIKE** BASE-BALL.

WHAT'S **THAT** GOT TO DO WITH IT? DOES YOUR MOTHER LIKE **BRIDGE**? DO I LIKE **BOWLING**? **WE** LIVE UP TO OUR RESPONSIBILITIES!

BUT I DON'T **WANT** TO PLAY BASE-BALL.

DO I **WANT** TO BELONG TO THE **COMMUNITY CENTER**? **I** GET **ALONG**! THAT'S PART OF BEING **GROWN UP**! LEARNING TO BE **HAPPY** AT DOING WHAT YOU DON'T WANT TO DO!

BUT I **HATE** BASEBALL.

MY WIFE AND I HAD BROKEN UP, MY JOB WAS GOING DOWN THE DRAIN AND I WAS DEVELOPING A DRINKING PROBLEM. I SAW MYSELF AS A LATENT FAILURE.

SO ONE DAY I SAT DOWN AND ASKED MYSELF **WHY.** AN INTELLIGENT MAN SHOULD BE ABLE TO WORK THROUGH HIS PROBLEMS.

THE FIRST ANSWER I CAME UP WITH WAS THE ARMS RACE, THE BERLIN CRISIS AND THE FEAR OF OVERPOPULATION. BUT I FELT THAT, WHILE TRUE, THIS WAS BASICALLY AN *EVASION.*

MY SECOND ANSWER WAS THAT IT WAS A PLOT ON THE PART OF MY ENEMIES TO CRUSH ME BECAUSE OF MY BEING SO BRIGHT. WHILE NO DOUBT IN PART TRUE, I FELT THAT THIS **TOO** WAS AN EVASION.

THEN I HIT ON THE ANSWER I'D BEEN AVOIDING ALL ALONG. THE ROOT OF MY FAILURE LAY IN MY UNHAPPY CHILDHOOD.

SO I WENT INTO ANALYSIS AND FOUND OUT THAT I HAD A VERY **HAPPY** CHILDHOOD.

THEREFORE, CONSIDERING MY BACKGROUND, MY INTELLECT AND MY ABILITY TO SEE THROUGH MY OWN EVASIONS AS EVIDENCE, I PROVED TO MYSELF THAT DESPITE MINOR SETBACKS I WAS **MISTAKEN** IN MY PREVIOUS SELF-ANALYSIS. I WAS **NOT** A FAILURE!

RESEARCH PROVES I'M A **SUCCESS!**

A TOASHT!

HELLO? MR. MILES TOOMUCH, THE JAZZ MUSICIAN? THIS IS THE **STATE DEPT.-BUREAU OF IMAGES** - VICTOR VENEER SPEAKING. I'M CALLING, SIR, IN REGARD TO THE ATTORNEY GENERAL'S PLAN FOR IMPROVING OUR IMAGE ABROAD BY SENDING OVER OUR INTELLECTUAL AND ARTISTIC **ELITE** - OH, YES, YOU ARE, MR. TOOMUCH! - WELL, **WE** SAY SO!

ANYHOW, WE DOWN HERE AT **IMAGE** JUST WANTED TO CHECK YOU OUT ON SOME DIFFICULT QUESTIONS YOU MIGHT BE ASKED ON YOUR TRIP- YOU KNOW- BY RIOTING STUDENTS OR SOMETHING.
FOR INSTANCE WHAT WOULD YOU SAY ABOUT OUR RESUMPTION OF ATMOS-PHERIC TESTING?

OH, YOU'D SAY **THAT** WOULD YOU? AND HOW WOULD YOU HANDLE DIVISIVE QUESTIONS ON RACE RELATIONS?- I SEE -. AND ABOUT OUR BERLIN, NATO AND ASIAN POLICIES?- — MMM - HMMMM -

WELL, MR. TOOMUCH, INSTEAD OF ALL **THAT** COULDN'T YOU JUST **PLAY** SOMETHING ON YOUR HORN?

I MEAN ISN'T **MUSIC** TRULY THE BEST COMMUNICATOR?

HEAVENS, **NO** ONE IS TRYING TO SUPPRESS YOU, MR. TOOMUCH, BUT IT **IS** SORT OF **YOUR** IMAGE OF OUR IMAGE AGAINST **OUR** IMAGE OF OUR IMAGE, ISN'T IT? AND SHOULDN'T IMPORTANT DECISIONS ON IMAGE BE LEFT IN THE HANDS OF THE PUBLIC RELATIONS EXPERTS WHO MAY HAVE ACCESS TO CLASSIFIED PUBLICITY THAT YOU DON'T KNOW ABOUT?

WELL, LOOK, MR. TOOMUCH, BEFORE WE REISSUE YOU YOUR PASSPORT WHY DON'T I SEND YOU OUR SAMPLE IMAGE SALES KIT, INCLUDING PAMPHLETS, FILM STRIPS AND VISUAL AIDS — ALL UNDER THE GENERAL TITLE OF "**OPERATION: GOOD GUY.**" WE'D LIKE YOU TO HAVE THE RIGHT SLANT BEFORE YOU WENT ABROAD, SIR.

AFTER ALL **IMAGE** IS **EVERYBODY'S** JOB.

ONCE AGAIN FROM THE
SUB-SUB BASEMENT OF
THE TIME-LIFE
BUILDING IN LITTLE OLD
NEW YORK, CLUB
MEGATON, THE **FUN**
FALLOUT SHELTER
BRINGS YOU THAT
EVER-SAFE SINGER
OF SONGS - **CLYDE
CONELRAD** - LET'S
HEAR IT, CLYDE!

I WANTED YEW TO COME
UNDERGROUND
YEW WANTED ME
TO COME OUT THERE-ERE-

YEW SAID OUR CHI-ILD
NEEDED NATURE'S GREENERY-
SUN AND SCENERY
I SAID KIDS ARE KIDS
ANY WHERE-ERE

YEW SAID GOODBYE
AND I DUG A HOLE
UNDERGROUND
YEW MARCHED
AWAY
WITH A PICKET SI-IGN.

BUT WHEREVER YOU GO
I'LL WAIT IN MY HOVEL
TILL THAT GOLDEN DAY
WHEN YEW'LL APPEAR
WITH A SHOVEL
IN OUR FALLOUT LOVE NEST
UNDERGROUND!

WONDERFUL, CLYDE -
THIS IS RADIO FREE
ACTIVE SIGNING OFF
WITH THIS ONE
REMINDER- "THE
HOLE WE DIG
MAY BE OUR OWN"

THE
LATEST
NEWS
AND
WEATHER
WILL
FOLLOW-

WHEN FIRST
I DANCED
IT WAS
MY MEANS
OF COMMUNI-
CATING
WITH THE
WORLD.

WHEN I DID **THIS** AND **THIS** I WAS SAYING TO THE WORLD THAT MAN MUST LIVE IN HAPPINESS AND PEACE AND MUTUAL LOVE.

BUT THE WORLD MISINTER-PRETED AND SAID I WAS **OBSCURE.**

I GREW
BITTER
TOWARD
THE
WORLD.
WHEN
NEXT I
DANCED
IT WAS FOR
NEUROTIC
SELF-
EXPRESSION

WHEN I DID **THIS**
AND **THIS**
I WAS TELLING THE
WORLD THAT IT
COULD GO ITS WAY
AND I WOULD GO
MINE.

BUT THE
WORLD
MISINTERPRETED
AND SAID
I WAS
OBSCENE.

NOW I'VE
WITHDRAWN
BEYOND
THE NEED
FOR
COMMUNI-
CATION.

WHEN I NOW DO
THIS AND
THIS
IT'S OUT
OF SHEER
BOREDOM.

CHA
CHA
CHA

THE WORLD
THINKS
I'M A
THRILL
CRAZY
KID.

EVER SINCE THEY WERE LITTLE I TOLD THEM—THEY'D GROW UP, THEY'D LEAVE US, THEY'D BREAK OUR HEARTS. DID I OR DIDN'T I TELL THEM?

THAT'S THE WAY CHILDREN ARE TODAY. THEY DON'T LISTEN.

AND WHAT DID THEY SAY? "NO, PA! NO! WE'LL **ALWAYS** LOOK AFTER YOU!" DID THEY OR DIDN'T THEY?

CHILDREN ALWAYS HAVE TO CONTRADICT.

I HAD TO SLIP **NOTES** UNDER THE DOOR—"DON'T TELL **ME** YOU WON'T BREAK OUR HEARTS. **I'M** YOUR FATHER!"

NOTES IN A FAMILY. WHO TAUGHT THEM HOW TO READ?

BUT I TOLD THEM. DIDN'T I? HUNDREDS OF TIMES. DIDN'T I? "**NO**" THEY SAID, "WE'LL **NEVER** LEAVE YOU." THEN THEY'D CLOSE THE DOOR TO THEIR ROOMS.

SECRETS IN A FAMILY. WHO BROUGHT THEM INTO THE WORLD?

SO ONE DAY IT'S "WE'LL NEVER LEAVE YOU" AND THE **NEXT** DAY IT'S "DON'T I HAVE THE RIGHT TO A LITTLE **PRIVACY**?"

PRIVACY! — WHO PAID THEIR DOCTOR BILLS?

SO THEY GREW UP. AND THEY **LEFT** US. SO WHO WAS RIGHT? THE FATHER OR THE CHILDREN?

A CHILD RIGHT? **HOW** — COULD A CHILD BE RIGHT?

BUT A **FUNNY** THING HAPPENED. THEY **DIDN'T** BREAK MY HEART. AS A MATTER OF FACT I FELT A **WHOLE LOT** BETTER.

ME TOO. ONE — HUNDRED PER CENT!

AFTER ALL THESE YEARS WHAT A DISCOVERY TO MAKE—

WE NEVER — LIKED CHILDREN.

DEAR MOTHER—
ARRIVED IN CAMP THIS A.M.
RECEIVED SIX SHOTS AND AN
INDOCTRINATION LECTURE
ABOUT DEFENDING THE FREE
WORLD. I
WANT TO
COME HOME—

DEAR SON—
BE A MAN. YOU ARE
ALWAYS WITH US IN
OUR HEARTS. WE ARE
SURE YOU'LL GET
USED TO IT—

DEAR MOTHER—
THIS A.M. THEY SHOWED US FILMS
ABOUT THE ENEMIES OF THE FREE
WORLD. THEY ARE ALL FROM THE
UNIVERSITY OF CALIFORNIA. ONE
OF THE FELLOWS IN OUR
BARRACKS COMES
FROM THERE. WE
ARE HIDING HIM.
I WANT TO
COME HOME—

DEAR SON—
TELL YOUR SERGEANT WE'D
ONLY SEND YOU TO A <u>GOOD</u>
SCHOOL. BE A MAN. <u>DON'T</u>
ASSOCIATE WITH
TROUBLEMAKERS.
YOU ARE ALWAYS
WITH US IN OUR
HEARTS—

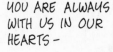

DEAR MOTHER-
MARCHED TO AND FROM THE CHURCH
OF OUR CHOICE THIS A.M. AND GIVEN
OUR 12TH INDOCTRINATION LECTURE.
CAPTAIN TOLD US WE IN THE FREE
WORLD MUST DEFEND
OURSELVES AGAINST
ENEMIES FROM WITHIN.
EVERYONE WHO
CHOSE WRONG
CHURCH OF HIS
CHOICE RECEIVED A
STERN WARNING. I
WANT TO COME HOME—

DEAR SON-
I'M SURE YOUR CAPTAIN IS
ONLY INTERESTED IN WHAT'S
BEST FOR YOU AND, AS DO
WE, HAS YOU ALWAYS WITH
HIM IN HIS HEART.
ASK HIM TO
CHECK OFF
THE RIGHT
CHURCH FOR
US TO GO TO.
BE A MAN.

DEAR MOTHER-
RECEIVED OUR 25TH INDOCTRINATION LECTURE
THIS A.M. FROM A NEW CAPTAIN. HE SAID THE
ARMY WAS LIBERALIZING ITS INFORMATION
PROGRAM AND ENCOURAGED US TO ASK QUES-
TIONS. I ASKED HIM TO
DEFINE "FREE WORLD". THE
CAPTAIN CALLED ME A PINKO
COLLEGE WISE GUY, ORDERED
ME ON EXTRA DETAIL,
AND WANTED TO KNOW
WHAT KIND OF FAMILY
I CAME FROM. I WANT
TO COME HOME—

DEAR SON-
IF YOU CAME HOME NOW THEY'D ONLY
FOLLOW YOU TO FIND US. DON'T TELL
THEM A THING UNTIL WE'RE ABLE
TO MOVE AND CHANGE OUR NAME.
PLEASE FOR OUR SAKE
STOP MAKING TROUBLE
AND BE A MAN!
WHEREVER WE GO
YOU AND YOUR ARMY
WILL ALWAYS BE
WITH US IN OUR
HEARTS.

NOW THEN, THE PROBLEM IS THE IMPROVEMENT OF INTELLIGENCE OPERATIONS BETWEEN OURSELVES AND **RUSSIER**, OURSELVES AND **ASIER**, AND (MORE DIFFICULT BECAUSE IT'S A CLOSED SOCIETY) OURSELVES AND **CIA**. YES, ED—

WELL, WE'VE HAD SOME SUCCESS IN TRACKING CIA'S ACTIVITIES BY MONITORING THE ENEMY'S RADIO ACCUSATIONS, CHIEF.

TRUE. HOWEVER, **STATE** TELLS ME IT FINDS IT INCREASINGLY FRUSTRATING TO RECOGNIZE A **NEW** GOVERNMENT IN THE **MORNING** ONLY TO HAVE **CIA** TRY TO OVERTHROW IT IN THE **AFTERNOON**. NOW, THAT'S **SLOPPY**.

IN TERMS OF LONG RANGE PLANNING **CIA** SHOULD, ON OCCASION, HAVE THE SAME FOREIGN POLICY AS **STATE**, WOULDN'T YOU SAY, CHIEF?

I'LL BUY THAT, WALT. TYPE UP A CLASSIFIED MEMO AND LEAK IT TO THE PRESS. NOW AFTER LUNCH I WANT TO DISCUSS POSSIBLE SITES FOR A FUTURE SERIES OF ATMOSPHERIC TESTS. I UNDERSTAND THAT SOMEBODY SUGGESTED HAVANA—

BON APPETIT, CHIEF—

THE PRESIDENT
DROPPED BY FOR
BREAKFAST
YESTERDAY. VERY
UNEXPECTED.

WHY, OF COURSE. YOUR
HOUSE IS ON THE WAY
TO **MY** HOUSE. WE
HAD LUNCH.

I TOLD HIM I WAS
WRITING MY THURS-
DAY COLUMN ON
EXECUTIVE POWER.
I THINK IT'S THE
KEY TO **EVERY-
THING**!

OH, IS **THAT** WHERE HE PICKED
THAT UP? I SHOWED HIM MY
FRIDAY COLUMN ON THE
COMMON MARKET. **THAT'S**
THE KEY TO EVERYTHING.

HE SEEMED TERRIBLY
INTERESTED. HE SAID
WE COULD DISCUSS
IT FURTHER AT THE
WHITE HOUSE .RECEPTION
FOR KATHERINE ANNE
PORTER.

THE COMMON ·MARKET!
THE ENTIRE FREE WORLD
INCORPORATED INTO A
TARIFF FREE EXCHANGE
OF MISSILE WARHEADS! A
NATO ALLIANCE
FOR PROGRESS!
I TOLD
HIM!

POWER, I TOLD HIM. THE DEVIOUS INFLUENCE OF POWER! HE READ MY COLUMN WITH **AVID** INTEREST. EVEN FASTER THAN USUAL.

OF COURSE—HE ALWAYS SAYS TO ME—"JOE, NO MATTER HOW FAST I READ, YOU ALWAYS FINISH THE PAGE AHEAD OF ME."

"MR. PRESIDENT," I SAID (THOUGH I'VE KNOWN HIM FOR YEARS I STILL REFER TO HIM BY HIS CEREMONIAL TITLE), "IF I HAVE HELPED FORM POLICY IN ANY WAY— AS A NEWSPAPER MAN I'D RATHER NOT KNOW ABOUT IT."

"WELL SAID, SCOTTY." HE REPLIED.

"JOE," HE LEAKED TO ME, "YOU'RE WORTH FIFTEEN DEAN RUSKS." "COME OFF IT, SIR" I ANSWERED, "I AM BUT A NEWSPAPERMAN"

I **AM** THE NEW FRONTIER.

NO, YOU'RE NOT! IT'S **ME!**

OUR SUBJECT TODAY IS **URBAN ARCHITECTURE** OF THE NINETEENTH AND TWENTIETH CENTURIES—BASED ON EXCAVATION AND RECONSTRUCTION OF THE RUINS OF THAT PERIOD IN HISTORY.

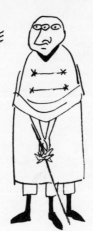

OF COURSE, WITH THE EVIDENCE OF SO MUCH TOTAL DESTRUCTION WE ASSUMED THE RUINS WERE CREATED BY **WAR**— UNTIL A CHANCE DISCOVERY OF A HIDDEN DOCUMENT PROVED THAT IT WASN'T WAR AT ALL— IT WAS A **GUERILLA** INSURRECTION—SOMETHING CALLED "**URBAN RENEWAL**"

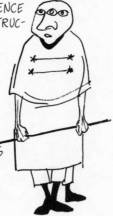

OUR FIRST SLIDE SHOWS A RECONSTRUCTION OF THE EARLIEST AND MOST **PRIMITIVE** FORM OF THAT PERIOD— THE **GLASS SLAB**— BUILT PROBABLY IN THE MIDDLE NINETEENTH CENTURY— NOTICE ITS **VACUOUSNESS** AND LACK OF SCALE.

NEXT WE HAVE A **LATER**, MORE **TRANSITIONAL** HOUSE OF THE EARLY TWENTIETH CENTURY- **STILL** RATHER MONOTONOUS BUT FEATURING GREATER SOPHISTICATION OF **DETAIL**. THE RECORDS WE FOUND PROVE THAT THESE CONSTRUCTIONS WERE AT FIRST KNOWN AS "**HOUSING PROJECTS**," A CLUMSY TERM LATER SIMPLIFIED INTO "**SLUMS**."

OUR **LAST** SLIDE REPRESENTS A **HIGH** POINT OF PROGRESS. BUILT IN THE LATE TWENTIETH OR EARLY TWENTY-FIRST CENTURY THIS BUILDING KNOWN AS A "**BROWNSTONE**" UTILIZES A TASTE AND A FLAIR FOR EXPERIMENTATION THAT SUGGEST AN ARCHITECTURAL RENAISSANCE.

ONE CAN ONLY BE LEFT BREATHLESS BY THE BRILLIANCE OF A SOCIETY THAT WAS ABLE TO MAKE SUCH GIANT STRIDES IN A MERE ONE-HUNDRED FIFTY YEARS.

DO YOU KNOW HOW LONG ITS BEEN SINCE I'VE HAD A MEANINGFUL RELATIONSHIP?

HOW LONG? HOW LONG?

TWO YEARS! FOR **TWO** WHOLE YEARS I'VE BEEN AFRAID OF HAVING A MEANINGFUL RELATIONSHIP.

TWO YEARS! DO YOU KNOW HOW LONG ITS BEEN SINCE **I'VE** HAD A MEANINGFUL RELATIONSHIP?

HOW LONG? HOW LONG?

NEVER.

NOT **NEVER!**

NEVER! I MEAN **NEVER.** LIKE THERE WERE TIMES WHEN I **THOUGHT** MY RELATIONSHIP WAS MEANINGFUL BUT WHEN IT WAS OVER I COULD SEE IT WASN'T MEANINGFUL AT **ALL.** IT WAS JUST **MAKING OUT.**

I **DESPISE** JUST MAKING OUT.

I AGREE. YOU TAKE SEX OUT OF CONTEXT AND IT'S JUST **HELL!**

SOMETIMES I WANT SO HARD FOR A RELATIONSHIP TO BE MEANINGFUL THAT I READ MEANINGFUL THINGS INTO IT —

— AND THEY'RE NOT **THERE!** THAT'S **FALSE MEANINGFULNESS!** I DO THAT **ALWAYS!**

AND THEN I GET BITTER AND **BLAME** PEOPLE WHEN **ACTUALLY** IT'S NOT **ANYBODY'S** FAULT.

A MEANINGFUL RELATIONSHIP CAN **NOT BE** BUILT ON BLAME. IF IT TURNS OUT TO BE JUST MAKING OUT I GUESS ALL ONE CAN DO IS **ACCEPT** IT.

I'D HATE FOR IT TO BE MAKING OUT WITH **US,** BERNARD.

I COULDN'T STAND IT, DOROTHY. BUT **WHAT** CAN WE DO? WE CAN'T RUN **AWAY.**

I THINK I LOVE YOU, BERNARD.

I THINK I LOVE **YOU,** DOROTHY.

WELL, WHAT DO YOU THINK? \

WE'LL JUST HAVE TO **WATCH** OURSELVES EVERY MINUTE.

MY DREAM HAS ALWAYS BEEN TO WRITE A NOVEL ON THE CULTURAL BREAKDOWN OF THE MIDDLE CLASS.

BUT I'VE LONG FELT AN INABILITY TO COMMUNICATE. WHEN ALL IS SAID AND DONE- DO I **REALLY** KNOW PEOPLE?

SO I TOOK LEAVE OF THE UNIVERSITY AND ASSUMED AN OFFICE POSITION FEELING THAT THE PRESSURE OF DAILY CONTACT WOULD LEND ME INSIGHTS INTO THE ORIENTATION, HABITS AND GROUP NEEDS OF MY FELLOW WORKERS.

BUT I COULDN'T COMMUNICATE WITH THEM. WHEN I TRIED TO LEAD DISCUSSIONS ON THE CULTURAL BREAKDOWN OF THE MIDDLE CLASS ALL **THEY'D** TALK ABOUT WAS **BASEBALL**.

SO I PUT ASIDE THE NOTES FOR MY NOVEL AND BONED UP ON THE SPORTS PAGE FINDING THAT, IN TIME, I WAS READY TO SUBTLY LEAD OFFICE CONVERSATION FROM BASEBALL AS A SPORT TO BASEBALL AS A FACTOR IN THE CULTURAL BREAKDOWN OF THE MIDDLE CLASS.

BUT AT THAT POINT THE **FOOTBALL** SEASON BEGAN. SO IN ORDER TO RE-ESTABLISH RAPPORT I HAD TO ABANDON THE NOTES FOR MY NOVEL AND BONE UP ON THE SPORTS PAGE TILL I FOUND MYSELF READY TO SUBTLY MANIPULATE OFFICE DISCUSSION INTO THE INTER-RELATIONSHIP BETWEEN BASEBALL, FOOTBALL AND THE CULTURAL BREAKDOWN OF THE MIDDLE CLASS.

WHICH IS WHEN THE BASKETBALL SEASON BEGAN.

AND SOON AFTER— ICE HOCKEY.

I'VE FINALLY HAD TO ABANDON MY NOVEL. IN ANY EVENT ITS ALL BEGUN TO SEEM A BIT SUPERFICIAL. BESIDES I'M **MUCH** TOO BUSY KEEPING UP WITH THE SPORTS PAGE.

HOWEVER I **AM** COMMUNICATING EXTREMELY WELL.

EVER SINCE I WAS A LITTLE KID I DIDN'T WANT TO BE ME. I WANTED TO BE BILLIE WIDDLEDON. AND BILLIE WIDDLEDON DIDN'T EVEN **LIKE** ME.

I WALKED LIKE **HE** WALKED. I TALKED LIKE **HE** TALKED. I SIGNED UP FOR THE HIGH SCHOOL **HE** SIGNED UP FOR—

WHICH WAS WHEN BILLIE WIDDLEDON CHANGED. HE BEGAN TO HANG AROUND HERBY VANDEMAN. HE **WALKED** LIKE HERBY VANDEMAN. HE **TALKED** LIKE HERBY VANDEMAN.

HE MIXED ME UP! I BEGAN TO WALK AND TALK LIKE BILLIE WIDDLEDON WALKING AND TALKING LIKE HERBY VANDEMAN.

AND THEN IT DAWNED ON ME THAT HERBY VANDEMAN WALKED AND TALKED LIKE JOEY HAVERLIN AND JOEY HAVERLIN WALKED AND TALKED LIKE CORKY SABINSON.

SO HERE I AM WALKING AND TALKING LIKE BILLIE WIDDLEDON'S IMITATION OF HERBY VANDEMAN'S VERSION OF JOEY HAVERLIN TRYING TO WALK AND TALK LIKE CORKY SABINSON.

AND **WHO** DO YOU THINK CORKY SABINSON IS ALWAYS WALKING AND TALKING LIKE? OF **ALL** PEOPLE— DOPEY KENNY WELLINGTON—

THAT LITTLE PEST WHO WALKS AND TALKS LIKE ME.

GIL! DO THESE OLD EYES **DECEIVE** ME? I HAVEN'T SEEN **YOU** SINCE THE OLD "YOUTH **FOR TOMORROW**" DAYS THIRTY YEARS AGO!

WHAT A FACTIONALIST RAT RACE **THAT** WAS, EH, DAN BOY?

THAT WAS **NOTHING!** YOU SHOULD HAVE JOINED "**STUDENTS FOR CHANGE**" THAT FOLLOWED IT FIVE YEARS LATER —

OH, I JOINED! I JOINED! WAS **THAT** EVER A FACTIONALIST RAT RACE!

WELL, **ONE** GOOD THING CAME OUT OF IT- "**BUDDIES FOR BETTERMENT**". **THEY**, AT LEAST, HAD SOME UNITY —

UNTIL IT DETERIORATED INTO A FACTIONALIST RAT RACE.

I JOINED ONE OF THE SPLINTER GROUPS— "JUNIORS FOR JUSTICE". YOU WEREN'T ACTIVE IN THAT ONE, WERE YOU, GIL?

NO, I HAD TO TEMPORARILY DROP OUT OF THE YOUTH MOVEMENT. MY WIFE WAS HAVING HER FOURTH BABY. BUT I HEAR IT DEVELOPED INTO A FACTIONALIST RAT RACE.

WELL, **EVERYTHING** FELL APART FOR AWHILE. A LOT OF THE YOUTH **WE** KNEW BEGAN RETIRING OR GOING ON PENSION. **NEW** FACES CAME IN. **NEW** YOUTH— INEXPERIENCED. DISRESPECTFUL. **UNTHEORETICAL.**

DIRECTION- LESS!

THEY **NEED** DIRECTION! I'VE BEEN TRYING TO GET MYSELF INTO "**PROGENY FOR PEACE**" BUT—I DON'T KNOW—FOR SOME REASON THEY DON'T SEEM TO **WANT** ME.

THAT'S THE TROUBLE WITH KIDS TODAY. NO SENSE OF HISTORY.

WILLIE - COME OUT OF **THERE!** YOU'VE BEEN IN THERE LONG **ENOUGH!**

SOON MA. SOON—

NOT SOON, WILLIE. **NOW!** WHAT ARE YOU DOING IN THERE ALL BY YOURSELF **ANY**HOW?

READING, MA. READING—

YOUR FATHER DIDN'T GET A **BANK** LOAN TO BUILD **YOU** A **LIBRARY**, MISTER! YOU DO YOUR READING SOMEWHERE **ELSE** THAN HIS FALLOUT SHELTER!

IT'S **MY** FALLOUT SHELTER **TOO**, MA!

ARGUMENTS! ARGUMENTS! YOU SAY IT'S **YOURS** - YOUR **SISTER** SAYS IT'S **HERS** - IT'S **EVERYBODY'S** FALLOUT SHELTER BUT **MAMA'S!**

YOU NEVER YELL AT SISTER WHEN **SHE'S** IN HERE.

YOUR SISTER DUCKS EVERY TIME SHE HEARS A **PLANE!** YOU HAVE TO MAKE **ALLOWANCES** FOR YOUR SISTER!

I'LL BE OUT IN A MINUTE—

WELL, CONGRATULATIONS, MISTER. YOU WEREN'T PLAYING WITH THE **MACHINE GUN** AGAIN WERE YOU?

HONEST, MA I WAS **READING.** I DIDN'T TOUCH **ANYTHING** OF DAD'S.

READING—READING—WHAT'S SO IMPORTANT THAT YOU WERE READING?

"YAHOO WORLD WAR III HOORAY COMICS".

THE **THINGS** THEY'RE ATTRACTED TO! WHAT CAN YOU **DO** WITH KIDS TODAY?

FOR YEARS THOSE OF US WHO
HAVE TOILED IN THE VINEYARDS
OF SUBURBAN CIVIL DEFENSE
HAVE BEEN CONCERNED WITH
THE PROBLEM OF HOW TO
MAINTAIN LAW AND ORDER
FOLLOWING A NUCLEAR ASSAULT.

THE BIG CITIES WOULD, OF COURSE,
BE ANNIHILATED, THEREBY
SIMPLIFYING **THEIR** CIVIL
DEFENSE PROBLEMS
IMMEASURABLY. HOWEVER,
FOR THOSE OF US IN **SUBURBIA**
THERE ARE **BOUND** TO BE
COMPLICATIONS.

WE WOULD BE SUBJECT TO
MASS ONSLAUGHTS OF
REFUGEES FROM THE CITY.
WHILE OUR HEARTS, AS
ALL HEARTS MUST, GO OUT
TO THESE VICTIMS THEY
DO POSE A THREAT TO
OUR CAREFULLY PLANNED
PROGRAM.

I **IGNORED** THE VOICE. I INVESTED **MORE**. I MADE A **LOT** OF MONEY. BUT THE **HIGHER** I WENT THE **SHAKIER** I FELT. THEN ONE DAY A COMMITTEE OF TOTAL STRANGERS CAME INTO MY OFFICE. "WHAT CAN I DO FOR YOU?" I ASKED, THINKING IT MIGHT BE ANOTHER GOOD CITIZENSHIP AWARD.

"YOU ARE A FRAUD, IRWIN CORPULENT," THEY SAID TO ME. "WE HAVE FOUND YOU OUT AND WE ARE TAKING IT ALL AWAY."

I CLEANED OUT MY DESK AND I LEFT.

WHEN THEY FIND YOU OUT THEY FIND YOU OUT. WHY ARGUE.

HELLO,
DOGGIE.

I'M AFRAID OF DOGS, DOGGIE.
I HAVE NOTHING AGAINST YOU
PERSONALLY. IT'S JUST **DOGS**
IN GENERAL I'M AFRAID OF —

BUT IT'S MY POLICY TO CULTIVATE
THOSE THINGS IN LIFE THAT I
FEAR THE MOST. I FEEL IF
YOU'RE **AFRAID** OF SOMETHING
IT'S ALWAYS
BEST TO
NEGOTIATE.

FOR INSTANCE, IF I PET
YOU WOULD **THAT** MAKE
US FRIENDS? **MAY** I
PET YOU? WOULD YOU
SNARL AT ME IF I
PET YOU?

I MADE GREAT FRIENDS WITH
A VERY HOSTILE CAT THIS
MORNING. IS IT **ALL RIGHT**
IF I PET YOU?

LAST WEEK I GOT A PARAKEET
TO SIT ON MY **FINGER.**
PARAKEETS, I'M TOLD, CAN TAKE
THE TRUE **MEASURE** OF A PERSON.
WILL YOU **BITE**
IF I PET YOU?

I'M GOING TO PET YOU **NOW**, DOGGIE.
YOU'LL SEE IT WILL BE ALL RIGHT
AND WE'LL BECOME **DEAR** AND
DEVOTED FRIENDS. I'M GOING TO PET
YOU **RIGHT** NOW. **THERE! I PET YOU!**

EVEN WHEN I'M ABLE TO
GIVE I FEEL I'M ONLY
BEING TOLERATED.

TRY TO SEE IT **MY** WAY. I **AM** NEARLY TWENTY AND IF I WAS **EVER** GOING TO MAKE THE BREAK **NOW** WAS THE TIME TO DO IT. IMAGINE, HALF MY GIRL FRIENDS WERE ALREADY SEPARATED FROM THEIR HUSBANDS AND HERE I WAS STILL LIVING AT **HOME!**

SO I TOLD MY PARENTS I WAS MOVING OUT.

YOU CAN'T **IMAGINE** THE YELLING AND SCREAMING. MY FATHER SAID - "YOU'RE BREAKING YOUR MOTHER'S HEART!" MY MOTHER SAID - "WHAT WAS MY CRIME? WHAT WAS MY **TERRIBLE** CRIME?"

AND BEFORE I KNEW IT WE WERE IN THE MIDDLE OF A BIG ARGUMENT AND I TOLD THEM THEY BOTH NEEDED ANALYSIS AND THEY TOLD ME I HAD A FILTHY MOUTH AND SUDDENLY I WAS OUT ON THE STREET WITH MY RAINCOAT, MY SUITCASE AND MY TENNIS RACKET BUT I HAD NO PLACE TO **MOVE!**

SO I LOOKED AROUND DOWNTOWN AND EVERYTHING WAS TOO EXPENSIVE AND EVENING CAME AND ALL MY GIRL FRIENDS HAD RECONCILED WITH THEIR HUSBANDS SO THERE WAS ABSOLUTELY NO PLACE I COULD SPEND THE NIGHT.

WELL, **FRANKLY**, WHAT ON EARTH COULD I **DO**? I WAITED TILL IT WAS **WAY** PAST MY PARENTS BEDTIME - THEN I **SNEAKED** BACK INTO THE HOUSE AND SET THE ALARM IN MY BEDROOM FOR SIX THE NEXT MORNING.

THEN I SLEPT ON TOP OF THE BED SO I WOULDN'T WRINKLE ANY SHEETS, SNEAKED SOME BREAKFAST IN THE MORNING AND GOT OUT BEFORE ANYONE WAS UP.

I'VE BEEN LIVING THAT WAY FOR TWO MONTHS NOW.

EVERY NIGHT AFTER MIDNIGHT I SNEAK INTO MY BEDROOM, SLEEP ON TOP OF THE BED TILL SIX THE NEXT MORNING, HAVE BREAKFAST AND SNEAK OUT.

AND EVERY DAY I CALL UP MY PARENTS FROM THE DOWNSTAIRS DRUGSTORE AND THEY YELL AND CRY AT ME TO COME BACK. BUT, OF COURSE, I ALWAYS TELL THEM NO.

I'LL **NEVER** GIVE UP MY INDEPENDENCE.

PEACE MARCHERS IN A **COMIC STRIP**? YOU **CAN'T** BE SERIOUS!

YES SIR! **THERE** THEY ARE MARCHING ON THIS MISSILE BASE THAT COLONEL CANYON IS IN COMMAND OF.

COLONEL CANYON? YOU MEAN **STEVE** CANYON? I THOUGHT HE WAS ONLY A **CAPTAIN!**

CAPTAINS HARDLY MAKE IT IN COMIC STRIPS ANYMORE. YOU REMEMBER HOW THEY USED TO DATE MAGAZINES MONTHS AHEAD SO YOU'D THINK THEY WERE **BETTER**? WELL, THAT'S HOW THEY RANK OFFICERS IN COMIC STRIPS. TERRY LEE MUST AT LEAST BE A **MAJOR** BY NOW. AND **BUZ SAWYER**—WELL, I'M AFRAID TO GUESS!

BUT STEVE CANYON OUTRANKS THEM ALL. **RIGHT**? NOBODY OUTRANKS STEVE CANYON—EXCEPT MAYBE PAT RYAN.

I DON'T KNOW HOW IT WORKS. TIME IN GRADE OR SOMETHING ANYHOW STEVE CANYON ISN'T A BLACK AND WHITE COLD WARRIOR LIKE THE **OTHER** COMIC STRIPS! HE TELLS THE PEACE MARCHERS THEY CAN PICKET ALL THEY WANT BECAUSE THAT'S THEIR RIGHT AS **AMERICANS.**

BUZ SAWYER WOULD **NEVER** DO THAT.

ALL HE ASKS THEM TO DO IS **PROVE** THEIR CITIZENSHIP: SHOW THEIR PASSPORTS OR THEIR FIRST PAPERS. OR SOMETHING.

SAY, THAT'S A **GREAT** IDEA!

SO **I** WAS THINKING THAT THE NEXT TIME THEY PEACE MARCH HERE AT THE WHITE HOUSE **WE** PULL THE SAME STUNT! IT WON'T BE THE **FIRST** TIME WE'VE BASED GOVERNMENT POLICY ON A COMIC STRIP.

MARVELOUS! BUT WHAT IF THEY CARRY PROOF WITH THEM?

YES. THEY'RE A FOXY BUNCH. THEY'RE **BOUND** TO AFTER AWHILE. WELL THEN—WHY DON'T WE MAKE THEM ALL TAKE LITERACY TESTS? IT WORKS WONDERFULLY WELL DOWN SOUTH.

COLONEL— I THINK YOU'VE OUT THOUGHT EVEN STEVE CANYON!

LET'S TURN TO MARY WORTH—SHE MAY HAVE SOME ADVICE ON OUR ASIAN POLICY.

I USED TO READ THEM ADS - KNOW WHAT I MEAN? "EVEN YOUR BEST FRIEND WON'T TELL YOU" ADS - AND IT USED TO BOTHER ME BE- CAUSE IF YOU'RE A **RIGHT** GUY - NICE TO YOUR MOTHER AND EVERYTHING - WHAT KIND OF GIRL IS IT WHO'D GIVE YOU THE GATE BECAUSE OF THE **WRONG** TOOTHPASTE YOU USE — OR WHAT KIND OF PHONEY FRIEND IS IT WHO'D SPEND HIS TIME NOT DRINKING WITH YOU BUT **SMELLING** YOU?

AND THEN IT WOULD BOTHER ME
HOW THESE PEOPLE IN THE ADS
WOULD BECOME POPULAR
OVERNIGHT BY CHANGING
BRAND NAMES. I
MEAN THEY DIDN'T
CHANGE THEIR **INSIDES**
AT ALL — THEY WEREN'T
BETTER PEOPLE. BUT
SUDDENLY THEY'D SWITCH
BRANDS AND BECOME
PRIDE OF THE
REGIMENT.

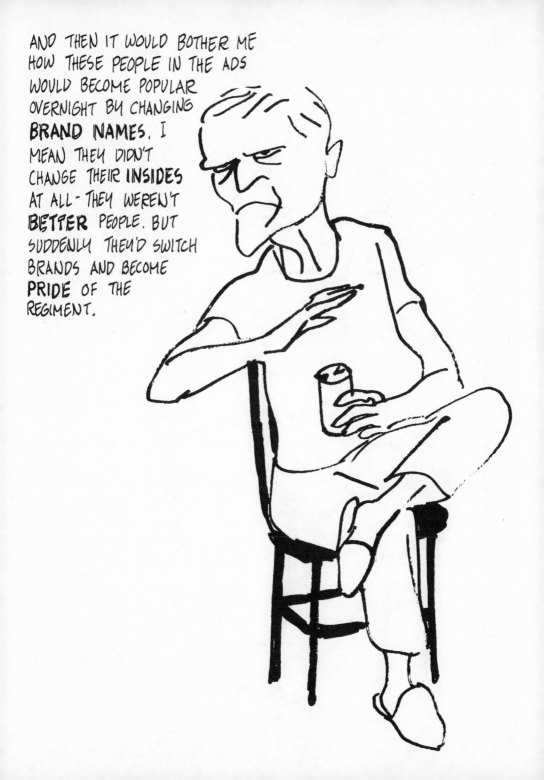

WELL THIS USED TO BOTHER ME BECAUSE, FRANKLY, PEOPLE NEVER **HAVE** TAKEN TO ME. LIKE AT THE JOB THE ONLY DESK DURING BREAKS WHERE YOU CAN'T HEAR A STEADY BUZZ-BUZZ OF CONVERSATION IS **MINE.** NOBODY **EVER** COMES OVER TO **ME!** I ALWAYS GOT TO GO OVER TO **THEM.** ALL MY LIFE.

WHEN I WAS A KID AND THREE OF US WOULD WALK DOWN THE STREET? **I'D** NEVER **ONCE** BE IN THE MIDDLE. I'D ALWAYS BE ON THE **GUTTER** SIDE — IN THE PATH OF APPROACHING BABY CARRIAGES! I NEVER GOT INVITED TO JOIN UP WITH ANY CLUBS. I WENT THROUGH THE ENTIRE ARMY WITHOUT **ONCE** BEING ASKED TO PLAY CARDS.

AND I ADMIT
SOMETIMES I
USED TO WAKE
UP IN THE MIDDLE
OF THE NIGHT
DRIPPING SWEAT-
AND GOING ON
AND OFF IN MY
HEAD LIKE A BIG
NEON SIGN WAS-
"BAD BREATH, BAD
BREATH, BAD
BREATH."

I GOT MARRIED AND MY WIFE
TREATED ME LIKE A **JANITOR.**
THE ONLY THING SHE COULD
SAY NICE FOR ME WAS THAT
I'M GOOD WITH MY HANDS.
WHEN THE OTHER WIVES
BOASTED ABOUT **THEIR**
HUSBANDS TALENTS SHE'D
CALL ME IN TO PUT UP A
SHELF. SO AT PARTIES I'D
DO MY FAMOUS "PUTTING UP
THE SHELF BIT" AND THE REST
OF THE TIME WE WERE
STRANGERS.

AND MORE AND
MORE IN THE BACK
OF MY HEAD IT
WENT-"CHANGE
YOUR SOAP. CHANGE
YOUR TOOTHPASTE"
BUT-I DON'T KNOW-
I ALWAYS FELT
THAT I'M ME FOR
BETTER OR WORSE.
I'M ME!

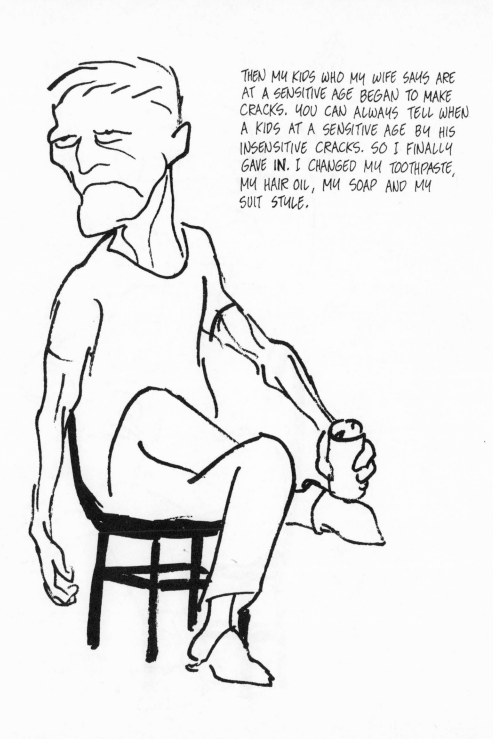

THEN MY KIDS WHO MY WIFE SAYS ARE
AT A SENSITIVE AGE BEGAN TO MAKE
CRACKS. YOU CAN ALWAYS TELL WHEN
A KIDS AT A SENSITIVE AGE BY HIS
INSENSITIVE CRACKS. SO I FINALLY
GAVE **IN**. I CHANGED MY TOOTHPASTE,
MY HAIR OIL, MY SOAP AND MY
SUIT STYLE.

AND, SON OF A GUN, THE ADS WERE RIGHT! · MY WIFE GLOWED AT ME. THE KIDS **LOVED** ME. SUDDENLY EVERYBODY WAS MY BUDDY FOR THE FIRST TIME IN MY LIFE! I FELT STRAINED AND PHONEY AND EVERYBODY **PRAISED ME!**

THREE
WEEKS OF
IT WAS
ALL I
COULD
TAKE. THEN
I WENT
BACK TO THE
OLD WAYS.

IF THEY
PREFER **THAT**
KIND OF GUY
TO ME THE
HELL WITH
THEM

WE HAVE FORGOTTEN
THAT THE BEST
TRAINING A PURELY
CINEMATIC ACTOR
CAN HAVE IS
SWIMMING —

HE LEARNS
GRAPHIC RHYTHM.
HE LEARNS
BALANCED
FLUIDITY. HE
LEARNS
PHYSICAL
PROJECTION.

BRANDO IN A WAY KNOWS
THIS. I SUSPECT THAT
SECRETLY HE SWIMS.
ELSE HOW COULD HE
COME CLOSEST
TO THAT
GREATEST OF
HERO-VIRILITY-
GODS THE
CINEMA HAS
YET PRODUCED —

—JOHNNY
WEISSMULLER.

STUDY THE ECONOMY
OF LANGUAGE IN THE
EARLY WEISSMULLER
CYCLE. THE **CLEAN**,
UNCLUTTERED
PLOT STRUCTURE —
THE **DARKS**
OF HIDDEN
PASSION —

—BETWEEN MAN
AND ALLIGATOR,
BETWEEN MAN
AND APE, BETWEEN
MAN AND ELEPHANT.
DOES NOT SOME
OF THIS ANTICI-
PATE TENNES-
SEE WILLIAMS?

THE NEO-BERGMANESQUE
RELIGIOUS THEME- THE
ALWAYS ALIENATED
TARZAN- UNABLE
TO TRULY
COMMUNICATE
IN A JUNGLE
NOT OF
HIS OWN
MAKING.

IN ANOTHER
SOCIETY MIGHT
HE NOT HAVE
BEEN
BYRON?

AND WHO BETTER THAN
WEISSMULLER CAN
PORTRAY THIS?
IMPASSIVE YET TENDER.
SWINGING THROUGH
TREES (HOW
CONSCIOUSLY
FREUDIAN)
WITH THE
CONTROLLED
ARTISTRY OF
THE TRUE MIME.

HAS THE
PLASTICITY
OF CINEMA
EVER BEEN
SHOWN TO
BETTER
EFFECT?

WITH THE DECLINE OF WEISSMULLER,
FOLLOWED BY THE RETIREMENT
OF BUSTER CRABBE FROM
THE FLASH GORDON
SERIALS, BASIC
CINEMA RECEIVED
A BLOW FROM
WHICH IT
IS ONLY
NOW BE-
GINNING TO
RECOVER.

WE'VE ALL HEARD OF THE RADICAL RIGHT
AND THE RADICAL LEFT. WITH US TONIGHT
IS A SPOKESMAN OF A GROUP WHOSE
VIEWS WE'VE HEARD VERY LITTLE
ABOUT: **THE RADICAL MIDDLE**.

GOOD MORNING.
GOOD AFTERNOON.
GOOD EVENING.

WOULD YOU
DESCRIBE
THE VIEWS
OF YOUR
ORGANIZ-
ATION,
SIR?

PROBABLY. THE RADICAL MIDDLE
THINKS IT'S TIME WE TOOK THE
INITIATIVE IN WORLD AFFAIRS,
WHILE DEPLORING THE IDEA OF
CHANGE FOR
MERE CHANGE'S
SAKE.

WE OPPOSE CONCESSIONS TO THE SOVIETS.
HOWEVER, WE FAVOR NEGOTIATIONS AND
STRONGLY SUPPORT THE U.N., WHILE WE
REJECT ITS INTERFERENCE WITH OUR BASIC
INTERESTS.

WE FAVOR ARMS CONTROL AND A
CONTINUED BUILDUP, A STRONG
CIVIL RIGHTS PROGRAM WITHOUT
THE UNDUE HASTE WHICH CREATES
DEEP SCARS.

THEN, SIR,
SUMMING UP
WISE, YOU'D
SAY YOUR
PHILOSOPHY
IS — ?

BOLD TIMES CALL FOR BOLD
ANSWERS. WITHIN REASON.
IN A MANNER OF SPEAKING.
MORE OR LESS.

THANK YOU,
SIR.

ON THE
OTHER
HAND—

ONCE THERE WAS A RICH MERCHANT WHO HAD
THREE HANDSOME YOUNG SONS TO WHOM HE
ONE DAY PRESENTED A GIFT OF THREE BOWS
AND THREE ARROWS.
"EACH OF YOU WILL SHOOT A SINGLE ARROW"
INSTRUCTED THE FATHER "IN THE
DIRECTION THAT YOUR ARROWS
FLY THERE WILL YOU FIND
YOUR FORTUNES."

THE ELDEST SON FOLLOWED HIS ARROW TO
WASHINGTON, MARRIED A BEAUTIFUL PRINCESS
AND BECAME A BELOVED RULER ADMIRED
FOR THE MANNER IN WHICH HE SOUGHT
WORLD PEACE AND SENT TROOPS TO ASIER.

THE MIDDLE BROTHER FOLLOWED **HIS** ARROW TO
WASHINGTON, MARRIED A BEAUTIFUL PRINCESS
AND BECAME A LEGAL SCHOLAR, A FRIEND OF
MINORITIES AND AN ADVOCATE OF A WIRE TAP BILL.

THE YOUNGEST BROTHER MARRIED A BEAUTIFUL PRINCESS
AND JUST HUNG AROUND FOR AWHILE. HE WAS TOO YOUNG
TO PLAY WITH BOWS AND ARROWS. HIS OLDER BROTHERS
CRIED "**COME TO WASHINGTON! COME TO WASHINGTON!**"
"BUT I CAN'T WORK THIS DARN THING!"
SAID THE YOUNGER BROTHER STILL
TOO UNCOORDINATED TO PUT THE
ARROW TO THE BOW.

"WE CAN'T HELP YOU" SAID THE OLDER BROTHER
PLACING THE ARROW IN HIS HAND,
"YOU MUST DO IT YOURSELF" SAID THE MIDDLE
BROTHER PLACING THE BOW IN THE PROPER POSITION,
"IT'S UP TO YOU" SAID BOTH BROTHERS AS THEY
SHOT THE BOW, THE ARROW AND THE
YOUNGER BROTHER ALL THE
WAY TO WASHINGTON.

MORAL: NO MATTER WHO YOU ARE
IT'S NICE TO HAVE EVERYTHING.

A DANCE
TO THE
NEW YEAR.

IN THIS DANCE
I HAVE
SYMBOLIZED
PEACE ON
EARTH AND
GOOD WILL
TO ALL MEN.

UM- I DON'T WANT YOU
TO THINK I MEAN
ANYTHING **FUNNY**
BY THAT STATEMENT-
I MEAN PEACE, YES-
BUT WITHOUT APPEASE-
MENT ON THE
AFOREMENTIONED
EARTH AND, NATURALLY,
GOOD WILL TO
ALL MEN.

UH-WAIT A MINUTE-BY
GOOD WILL I MEAN
THAT WE SHOULD
HAVE GOOD WILL TO
THOSE WHO ARE- YOU
KNOW- ALL MEN OF
GOOD WILL-

WAIT A MINUTE— BY **ALL** MEN I MEAN ONLY **THOSE** MEN WHOM WE RECOGNIZE AS WILLING TO BE **REASONABLE** AND SEE OUR SIDE AS WELL AS THEIR OWN—AS LONG AS THEY DON'T HAVE A DOUBLE STANDARD AND PRETEND TO BE NEUTRALISTS.

SO REALLY WHAT THIS DANCE SYMBOLIZES IS A **RESPONSIBLE, CAUTIOUS** APPROACH—

TO ARMS CONTROL ON EARTH AND FRUITFUL NEGOTIATION TO SOME MEN.

I CALL IT "THE BENDS."

WHEN DO YOU THINK IT'S COMING?
I DON'T KNOW. PRETTY SOON.
WHAT DO YOU THINK IT'LL BE OVER? BERLIN?
BERLIN - MAYBE. FORMOSA, MAYBE. VIET NAM, MAYBE. THEY'LL FIND SOMETHING.
ARE YOU GOING TO FIGHT?
IT WOULD SEEM THE PATRIOTIC THING TO DO. I HAVEN'T MADE UP MY MIND.
I'M GOING TO GO ALONG WITH OUR LEADERS. THEY HAVE ACCESS TO INFORMATION I DON'T HAVE.
OBVIOUSLY THEY MUST KNOW WHAT THEY'RE DOING. THEY ALL HAVE DEGREES.

SO BECAUSE IT WAS, YOU KNOW, MOTHER'S DAY I SAVED UP ALL MY ALLOWANCE AND I GOT, YOU KNOW, MY MOTHER A PRESENT.

SO ANYHOW SUNDAY IT WAS MOTHER'S DAY AND I WOKE UP EARLY TO SURPRISE MY MOTHER WITH HER PRESENT—

A DECK OF CARDS.

BUT BEFORE I COULD LIKE DO IT, MY MOTHER SAID—

"YOU ARE THE REASON THAT I AM A MOTHER SO WE ARE GOING TO MAKE THIS **YOUR** HOLIDAY."

SO MY MOTHER AND MY FATHER AND ME WENT TO A BIG ADVENTURE MOVIE WHICH THEY SAID I WOULD ENJOY, CALLED "HIROSHIMA MON AMOUR"

AND WE SAT IN THE BALCONY BECAUSE MY MOTHER SAID I COULD SEE BETTER THAT WAY AND ANYHOW SHE COULD SMOKE. THEN WE WENT OUT TO EAT.

AND BECAUSE IT WAS MY CELEBRATION I WAS MADE TO SIT AT THE HEAD OF THE TABLE AND HAD TO CUT MY OWN FOOD AND GOT THE LAMB CHOPS ON THE FLOOR. AND MY MOTHER SAID SEEING HOW IT WAS MOTHER'S DAY, I COULD AT LEAST **TRY**.

THEN WE CAME HOME AND I STILL DIDN'T GIVE MY MOTHER HER PRESENT SO I GAVE HER THE DECK OF CARDS AND MY FATHER LAUGHED AND SAID, " BOY, **THAT'S** SURE AS HELL APPROPRIATE!" SO THERE WAS A FIGHT. I THINK, ABOUT MY FATHER'S DRINKING.

AND MY MOTHER WANTED TO KNOW HOW MUCH I SPENT.

WHY CAN'T THERE BE MOTHER'S DAY IN THE SUMMER WHEN I'M AWAY IN CAMP.

WHEN I WAS VERY YOUNG I WAS TOTALLY
SELF-ORIENTED. I FELT THAT WHEN I
ENTERED A CROWDED ROOM I WAS REALLY
THE **ONLY**
PERSON
THERE.

AND THAT WHEN I
LEFT THE ROOM ALL
THE PEOPLE BEHIND
ME **CEASED** TO EXIST.

THEN AS I GREW A LITTLE OLDER AND
LEARNED DISAPPOINTMENT I DEVELOPED
THE **NEW** FEELING THAT WHEN I ENTERED
A CROWDED
ROOM—

—I WAS THE ONLY PERSON
WHO **WASN'T** THERE.

IN ALL OF LIFE IT SEEMED
TO ME THAT I WAS THE
LEAST REAL.

BUT OF COURSE GROWTH
IS A CONTINUING
PROCESS. AS
THE YEARS
WENT BY
I **MELLOWED**.
I NO LONGER
LOOKED AT
LIFE IN
ABSOLUTES.

NOWADAYS WHEN I ENTER A
CROWDED
ROOM—

I'M NOT SURE **ANY**
OF US ARE THERE.

WHAT I FIRST
FELL IN LOVE
WITH WAS
YOUR NON-
CONFORMITY.
YOUR CONTEMPT
FOR THE
MATERIAL
VALUES OF
SOCIETY.

WHAT I FIRST
FELL IN LOVE
WITH WAS
YOUR **CALM**-
YOUR ABILITY
TO MAKE
EVERY
EMERGENCY
SEEM ALMOST
NORMAL -

WHEN WE FIRST
MARRIED I
LOVED YOUR
REFUSAL TO
SURRENDER
TO THE
MOB-
YOUR
PURITY
OF
MOTIVATION.

WHEN WE FIRST
MARRIED I
LOVED YOUR
SERENITY
FOR THE
WAY IT
ALLAYED MY
DOUBTS -
STRENGTHENED
ME IN MOMENTS
OF **CONFUSION** -

BUT AFTER
HERBERT'S
BIRTH YOU
CHANGED-
YOU BECAME
SELFISH -
UNRELIABLE -

BUT AFTER
HERBERT'S BIRTH
YOU CHANGED-
YOU BECAME
COOL - YOU
BECAME
REMOVED -

YOU REFUSED TO
FACE THE FACTS
OF LIFE. YOU
INSISTED ON
BEING OUT OF
STEP JUST
FOR THE SAKE
OF BEING
NOTICED!

YOU WERE
ALOOF-
NO LONGER
THERE
WHEN I
NEEDED
YOU -

YOU IGNORED
OUR **NEEDS.**
EVERYONE
ELSE HAD
A NICE
HOME.
WE
DIDN'T.

YOU
BECAME
HARD-

OH, I **LOVED**
THAT EARLY
ZANY YOU!
WHY DID
YOU HAVE
TO **SPOIL**
IT AND
CHANGE?

HOW I COULD
LOVE YOU AGAIN
IF YOU WERE JUST
SERENE LIKE IN
THE **OLD** DAYS-

I HAD JUST GOTTEN A FAT BONUS FOR CREATING A NEW COPY APPROACH FOR OUR BIGGEST CIGARET ACCOUNT— NO DOUBT YOU'VE SEEN IT—

"MORE TAR- MORE NICOTINE - MORE **RISK** IN **FRONTIER** THE CIGARET THAT SEPARATES THE MEN FROM THE BOYS **!**"

WHEN SUDDENLY IT DAWNED ON ME THAT I HATED MY JOB. YEAR IN AND YEAR OUT WORKING WITH BRIGHT, IMAGINATIVE PEOPLE WHO USED THEIR INTELLIGENCE TO DIG UP **NEW** REASONS WHY THERE WAS NOTHING WRONG WITH THE WAY THEY EARNED AN INCOME.

SO I DECIDED TO QUIT.

I TOLD MY WIFE AND SHE SAID-"YOU'RE NOT IN COLLEGE ANYMORE" AND I TOLD MY CO-WORKERS AND THEY SAID-"YOU'LL **GROW UP**" AND I TOLD MY PARENTS AND THEY SAID-"FACE THE FACTS AND BE A **MAN**."

HOW COME ONLY **UNETHICAL** DECISIONS ARE CONSIDERED MATURE ?

SO I **QUIT**. AND I SAT HOME AND TRIED TO FIGURE OUT WHAT I WAS EQUIPPED TO DO THAT WOULD HAVE **SOME** SOCIAL VALUE IN THE WORLD AND **STILL** MAKE ME A LIVING.

AND THE ANSWER WAS **NOTHING**.

IT'S BEEN FOUR MONTHS NOW. OUR MONEY IS RUNNING LOW. PRETTY SOON I'LL HAVE TO GO BACK TO WORK.

BUT THE WAY I SEE IT, EVEN IF I **CAN'T** DO ANYTHING OF VALUE - IF I QUIT ONE JOB EVERY YEAR AND STAY UNEMPLOYED FOR EIGHT OR NINE WEEKS —

I CAN GO **TWO WHOLE MONTHS** A YEAR WITHOUT DOING **HARM**!

SOME MEN HAVE TO RETIRE BEFORE THEY CAN SAY THAT.

WHEN I GO OUTSIDE AND LOOK UP AT A CLEAR BLUE SKY I WANT TO **ENJOY** THAT CLEAR BLUE SKY —

BUT I ALWAYS KNOW INSIDE MYSELF THAT IF I **CATCH** MYSELF ENJOYING IT — THAT CLEAR BLUE SKY WILL SUDDENLY **RAIN** ON ME.

IF I'M HAVING A WONDERFUL TIME WITH A BOY AND SENSE THAT I'M BEGINNING TO FALL IN LOVE, I **KNOW** THAT IF I **CATCH** MYSELF ENJOYING THE IDEA OF FALLING IN LOVE HE'LL NEVER CALL AGAIN.

IF I ENJOY **ANYTHING** — MY JOB OR **ANYTHING** — AND IF I **CATCH** MYSELF ENJOYING IT — I'LL ALWAYS EITHER MAKE A MISTAKE OR GET FIRED.

SO I WORK AT NOT NOTICING WHAT'S AROUND ME AND IF I SUDDENLY FIND MYSELF ENJOYING SOMETHING - BEFORE IT CAN GO WRONG I KNOCK ON WOOD AND THINK OF THE WORLD'S TROUBLES.

THERE'S ONLY ONE TIME IT'S SAFE TO ENJOY AN EXPERIENCE -

AFTER IT'S OVER.

I'VE QUIT
GOING OUT.

WHAT IS THIS YOU'VE
QUIT GOING OUT BIT?
HOW CAN YOU QUIT
GOING OUT?

I'VE JUST **QUIT**, THAT'S
ALL. IT'S DISHONEST
AND I'M THROUGH.
THE **HELL**
WITH IT!

DIS**HONEST**?
WHAT DO YOU
MEAN
DIS**HONEST**?

ALRIGHT. A WEEK AGO I'M ASLEEP
IN BED- TWO IN THE MORNING -
AND THE **PHONE** RINGS -
THE **SEXIEST** VOICE
I'VE EVER HEARD!

SHE SAYS HER NAME IS **DARLENE**
AND SHE JUST FLEW IN FROM THE
COAST AND SHE'S A FRIEND OF A
FRIEND AND SHE HAS
NO PLACE TO STAY
AND CAN I PUT
HER UP FOR
THE NIGHT.

ALRIGHT. I KNOW **SOMETHING** MUST BE
WRONG - BUT I TELL HER TO COME OVER.
AN HOUR LATER SHE
ARRIVES. **THE MOST
BEAUTIFUL GIRL I
HAVE EVER SEEN!**
AND IN SHE COMES
WITH TWO BOTTLES
OF BRANDY AND
A DOZEN EGGS.

SHE WHIPS UP THE MOST **FABULOUS** BREAKFAST I'VE EVER TASTED. WE SIT AND TALK FOR **HOURS**. SHE'S READ **ALL** THE BOOKS I'VE READ — LOVES **ALL** THE MUSIC I LOVE — THE **BRIGHTEST**, MOST **SENSITIVE** GIRL I'VE EVER KNOWN!

ALONG TOWARD DAWN WE BEGIN TO NUZZLE A LITTLE. I BUILD A FIRE. SUDDENLY WE'RE **GRABBING** EACH OTHER! WARM? YOU WOULDN'T BELIEVE IT! AFFECTIONATE? YOU HAVE **NO** CONCEPTION!

IT WAS THE LOVELIEST, PUREST EXPERIENCE I EVER HOPE TO HAVE — A FANTASY COME **TRUE** — ME WITH THE MOST BEAUTIFUL, DELIGHTFUL GIRL IN THE WORLD — AND SHE **LOVES** ME! SHE LOVES **ME**!

AND ALL THAT TIME DO YOU KNOW WHAT I WAS THINKING?

WHAT?

"WAIT TILL I TELL THE FELLAS."

ALL MY LIFE PEOPLE
BEEN TELLING ME I
HAVE A MORAL OBLIGATION.

BEFORE THE WAR I
HAD A MORAL
OBLIGATION TO
FIGHT FASCISM.

DURING THE WAR I **OWED** IT
TO MY COUNTRY TO **JOIN**
THE ARMY.

AFTER THE WAR IT WAS
MY **DUTY** TO WORK
FOR **PEACE, INTE-
GRATION, DECENT
HOUSING** AND
**BETTER TELE-
VISION
PROGRAMS.**

SO I CAN'T BE
FOR SOMETHING
BECAUSE IT'S JUST
RIGHT ANYMORE.
I GOT TO BE
FOR IT BECAUSE
I'D **OWE** SOME-
BODY IF I
WASN'T.

I FEEL AS
IF I'M
LIVING IN
A MORAL
DEBTORS'
PRISON.

DON'T GET ME WRONG— I THINK IT'S **WONDERFUL** THAT YOU KIDS ARE PROTESTING AGAIN. BUT WHY DON'T YOU PICKET **THE RUSSIANS**?

WE **ARE**. PICKETING THE RUSSIANS.

DON'T GET ME WRONG— I **DEPLORE** THE APATHY THAT ONCE SWALLOWED OUR YOUTH, BUT AREN'T PICKET SIGNS THE CRUDEST FORM OF PUBLIC DEBATE?

WE'RE WILLING TO TALK.

DON'T GET ME WRONG— I **FAVOR** FULL DEBATE OF OUR GLOBAL POLICIES, BUT WON'T WE **HARM** OURSELVES BY SEEMING DIVIDED IN THE EYES OF THE REST OF THE WORLD?

THEN YOU'RE **AGAINST** PROTEST?

DON'T GET ME WRONG— I THINK IT'S **WONDERFUL** THAT YOU KIDS ARE PROTESTING AGAIN. BUT COULDN'T YOU FIND YOURSELVES **ANOTHER** FIELD?

WHAT WOULD YOU HAVE IN MIND?

I'LL ASK THE STATE DEPARTMENT TO DRAW UP SUGGESTIONS. IF WE CAN ONLY GET YOUTH TO JOIN IN **RESPONSIBLE** PROTEST IT CAN TEACH US **ALL** A VALUABLE LESSON—

DON'T GET ME WRONG—

NO SIR.

LIKE EVERYBODY ELSE I WAS
A SOCIALIST WHEN I WAS
IN COLLEGE DURING
THE TWENTIES—
"SOLIDARITY FOREVER"
"ORGANIZE THE WORKERS!"
"OVERTHROW THE GOVERN-
MENT!"

I WAS A LIBERAL WHEN I GOT
OUT OF COLLEGE IN THE
THIRTIES—"NEW DEAL RECOVERY"
"DOWN WITH BOOM AND BUST"
"UP THE C.I.O."

I WAS A COMMUNIST
DURING THE FORTIES—
"UNITED FRONT"
"FREE EARL
BROWDER"
"JAIL THE
TROTSKYITES."

I WAS A DUPE DURING THE
FIFTIES - "BUT I DIDN'T REALIZE-"
    "THEY USED ME-"
    "I'LL NEVER SIGN
        ANYTHING AGAIN-"

AND NOW IN THE SIXTIES I'M
A CONSERVATIVE -
    "KEEP RED CHINA OUT OF THE U.N."
        "OVERTHROW CUBA"
        "UP BARRY GOLDWATER."

IT'S GOOD TO SEE
I'M STILL IN
STEP WITH THE
COLLEGE KIDS.

"HOW TO WIN ARGUMENTS
ON YOUR SUMMER
TOUR OF EUROPE"
OR
"A GUIDE TO CONVER-
SATIONAL COUNTERFORCE"

ENGLAND: WHEN THEY BRING
UP HERMAN KAHN, EDWARD
TELLER AND NUCLEAR
DETERRENCE (85 POINTS),
COUNTER WITH ROY WELENSKY,
SOUTHERN RHODESIA AND
THE CONTINUED SALE OF ARMS
TO SOUTH AFRICA. (90 POINTS)

FRANCE: WHEN THEY BRING UP
THE C.I.A., CIVIL RIGHTS AND
THE RADICAL RIGHT (80 POINTS),
COUNTER WITH THE O.A.S.,
SUPPRESSION OF THE PRESS
AND PLASTIC BOMBS. (85 POINTS)

RUSSIA: WHEN THEY BRING UP THE STOCK MARKET, THE DECLINE OF CAPITALISM AND THE CUBAN FIASCO (75 POINTS), COUNTER WITH HUNGARY, FAILING CROPS AND MAO TSE-TUNG. (85 POINTS)

GERMANY: WHEN THEY BRING UP ALLIED INDECISION ON WEST BERLIN (35 POINTS), YOU MAY COUNTER WITH LATENT NAZISM AND THE FEAR OF A NEW HITLER—BUT IT WILL SCORE YOU NO POINTS—THEY HAVE NEVER HEARD OF EITHER.

A FINAL WORD OF ADVICE : THE BEST WAY TO ESCAPE TROUBLE ON YOUR TOUR OF EUROPE IS TO AVOID SPEAKING TO ANYONE WHO UNDERSTANDS ENGLISH.

ALOHA!

I FLED TO FREEDOM FROM EAST GERMANY. DON'T LOOK AT ME THAT WAY. I SAY I DID!

SO I GOT ACROSS THE BORDER AND THE ALLIED OFFICERS SAID, "MAN, WHAT ARE **YOU** DOING?" AND I SAID "YOU CAN SEE PLAIN WELL WHAT I'M DOING. I'M FLEEING TO FREEDOM."

"WELL, MAN, HOW CAN YOU FLEE TO FREEDOM?" THEY ASKED ME. "YOU GERMAN?" AND I REPLIED "NO SIR", "YOU CHINESE?" AND I REPLIED, "NO SIR", "YOU RUSSIAN, HUNGARIAN, ALBANIAN, CZECH, POLE, **SIBERIAN**?" AND TO ALL THAT STUFF I REPLIED "NO SIR." "WELL, THEN," THEY SAID "YOU **CAN'T** BE FLEEING TO FREEDOM."

BUT I WOULDN'T GO BACK SO THEY HAD TO FIGURE OUT WHERE TO SEND ME. THE FRENCH OFFICER SAID "MAN, WE **CAN'T** SEND YOU TO FRANCE. YOU MIGHT GET PICKED OFF AS AN ALGERIAN."

THE ENGLISH OFFICER SAID, "WE ALREADY GOT OUR TROUBLES IN **LONDON** — AND SOUTH AFRICA WOULDN'T HAVE YOU. AND WE AREN'T LIKELY TO SEND YOU ANY- WHERES **ELSE** IN AFRICA BECAUSE FOR ALL **WE** KNOW YOU COULD BE A KENYATTA OR SOMETHING."

AND THE AMERICAN OFFICER SAID, "WE **CAN'T** SEND YOU TO THE **SOUTH** BECAUSE IF YOU FLED TO FREEDOM **ONCE**, WHAT'S TO STOP YOU FROM BEING A TROUBLE MAKER AND TRYING IT AGAIN?

-AND WE CAN'T SEND YOU TO **CUBA** BECAUSE THAT'S NO LONGER PART OF THE **FREE WORLD.** THEY REPRESS WHITE FOLKS THERE **TOO.**" SO THEY ALL SAID, "WHY DON'T YOU BE A GOOD FELLOW AND GO BACK WHERE YOU CAME FROM?"

WELL, I DON'T KNOW, MAYBE I **WILL.** DURING A MORAL CRISIS BETWIXT FREEDOM AND SLAVERY I DON'T WANT TO BE THE ONE TO MAKE TROUBLE.

ALWEEZ S'PLEASH'R
T'BE HERE LAD'Z
AN' GEN'LM'N-
LIKE T'SING
A LI'L SONG I
WROTE 'SPECIALLY
F'YOU –
– snap snap
snap

SELLLLLLLF PIT PIT
PIT-TY PIT-Y! THE WORLD
IS FULL OF SELLLLLLF PITY-
CRYING INTO ITS BEER
BECAUSE IT'S SOON LEAVING HERE
GOING AWAY OUT THERE –
BOOM!

SMASHHHHHHED CIT CIT
CIT-TY CIT-Y! ALL WE'LL
HAVE IS SMASHHHHHHED CITY-
FALLOUT AND MUCH DEBRIS
FALLIN' ALL OVER ME
OH SAY CAN YOU SEE –
BOOM!

IF **I** GO, YOU GO, WE ALL GO, EARTH-
IF YOU SHOOT, I SHOOT
THEN **WHAT'S** IT ALL WORTH?
A VANISHED PLANET WITHOUT
PRIOR CONSULTATION
IS NO EXAMPLE OF
SELF DETERMINATION —

REFERENNNNNND ME
BEFORE YOU DECIDE
TO **END** ME
GIVE ME A PARTIAL SAY
WE'LL DO IT **YOUR** WAY ANYWAY
THEN WE CAN ALL SALUTE
AND SAY

BOOM!

S'BEEN A PLEASH'R
ENNERTAININ' YOU
LAD'Z AN' GEN'LM'N -
I ONLY HOPE ITS
BEEN AS MUCH FUN
FOR YOU AS ITS
BEEN F'ME -

snap snap snap

SO ONE PART OF ME SAID:
"I HATE THIS JOB!
I HATE IT!
I HATE IT!"

THEN ANOTHER PART OF ME SAID:
"REMEMBER YOUR WIFE —
TWO KIDS TO FEED —
HOME IN THE SUBURBS —"

SO ONE PART OF ME SAID:
"I'M STAGNATING! I ONCE
HAD SOME DREAMS! WHAT'S
HAPPENED TO MY LIFE?"

AND THE OTHER PART OF ME SAID:
"WASHING MACHINE
COLOR TV
REPAIRS IN THE ATTIC —"

SO ONE PART OF ME SAID:
"IT'S WRONG TO SPEND SEVEN
HOURS A DAY AT WHAT I HATE!
IT'S NOT FAIR! IT'S WRONG!"

THEN THE SECOND PART OF ME SAID:
"YOU'RE JUST PENT UP —
GO OUT AND DRINK —
BLOW OFF SOME STEAM —"

BUT I THOUGHT OF YOU HERE
ALONE ALL DAY — TAKING CARE
OF THE KIDS — MAKING DINNER —
WAITING UP FOR ME SO
PATIENTLY.

I KNEW I HAD TO COME HOME!

AND THAT'S WHY
I SLUGGED YOU.

WHEN I WAS A KID I NEVER COULD
UNDERSTAND IT WHEN MY FATHER
SHUT HIMSELF OFF IN THE BED-
ROOM AND PLAYED SOLITAIRE.
MY MOTHER'D ALWAYS SAY
"FATHER- **SOME** FATHER-
I'M BOTH MOTHER **AND**
FATHER TO THESE KIDS.

THEN, AFTER I GOT MARRIED AND **WE**
HAD KIDS I BEGAN TO SEE IT A LITTLE
BETTER. IT'S AS IF MARRIAGE IS
FOR THE **MOTHER** AND THE FATHER
IS LIKE THE UNCLE WHO VISITS
WITH THE **CANDY**- THEY'LL **PLAY**
WITH YOU BUT IT'S THE MOTHER
WHO **OWNS** THEM. THE FATHER
IS ONLY AN UNCLE.

AND WHEN THE KIDS GET OLDER YOU
EVEN LOSE THE **RANK** OF **UNCLE**.
THE WIFE SAYS -"I'VE GOT
THREE CHILDREN TO TAKE
CARE OF- MY HUSBAND
AND THE TWO LITTLE
ONES. **SOME** FAT JOKE.

SO WHAT HAPPENS WHEN YOU'RE ALMOST FORTY AND TREATED LIKE A LITTLE BOY IN YOUR OWN HOUSE? YOU BEGIN TO **FEEL** LIKE A LITTLE BOY - **THAT'S** WHAT HAPPENS! LIKE **TV** - YOU WANT TO WATCH WHAT **YOU** WANT TO WATCH NOT WHAT **THEY** WANT TO WATCH.

SO YOU START COMING HOME LATER AND LATER. YOU **DRINK** MORE - YOU LEARN HOW TO **BOWL**. AND ALL THE WHILE YOU SAY TO YOURSELF - "HERE I AM THIRTY EIGHT YEARS OLD AND **I** DON'T HAVE IT AS GOOD AS THE **OTHER** KIDS -

- I DON'T EVEN HAVE MY OWN ROOM."

ONE DAY ARNIE, MY HUSBAND, POINTED OUT TO ME THAT EVERY WORD I SAID SOUNDED **EXACTLY** LIKE MY MOTHER.

SO HE SENT ME BACK INTO ANALYSIS AND I WORKED ON IT FOR A YEAR.

BUT WHEN I THOUGHT I WAS BETTER ARNIE, MY HUSBAND, POINTED OUT TO ME THAT EVERY WORD I SAID SOUNDED EXACTLY LIKE MY **FATHER**.

SO HE SENT ME BACK INTO ANALYSIS AND I WORKED ON IT FOR A YEAR.

BUT WHEN I THOUGHT I WAS BETTER ARNIE - HE'S MY HUSBAND- POINTED OUT THAT EVERY WORD I SAID SOUNDED EXACTLY LIKE MY **ANALYST.**

SO HE HAD ME CHANGE ANALYSTS AND I WORKED ON IT FOR A YEAR. AND I WAS SURE I WAS BETTER.

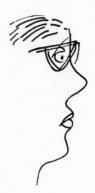

NOW ITS OVER SIX MONTHS AND EVERY WORD I SAY SOUNDS EXACTLY LIKE MY HUSBAND.

ARNIE THINKS I'M CURED.

TO START WITH I GOT MY-SELF A PARAKEET WHO WAS VERY FRIGHTENED AT FIRST.

BUT I TRAINED MY PARAKEET TO TRUST ME, TO LOVE ME, TO EAT OUT OF MY HAND.

THEN I GOT MY-SELF A DOG WHO WAS VERY NERVOUS AT FIRST.

BUT I TRAINED MY DOG TO TRUST ME, TO LOVE ME, TO DO ALL THE TRICKS I TAUGHT HIM.

NEXT I GOT MYSELF A CAT WHO WAS VERY WITHDRAWN AT FIRST.

BUT I TRAINED MY CAT TO TRUST ME, TO LOVE ME, TO COME ANYTIME I CALLED.

NOW I LIVE CONTENTEDLY WITH MY PARAKEET, MY DOG AND MY CAT. WE SPEND EVERY MINUTE OF THE DAY LEARNING TO RELATE. IT'S BEEN AN INVALUABLE EXPERIENCE.

PRETTY SOON I'LL BE READY FOR PEOPLE.